The
OLD CURIOSITY SHOP
IMMORTALIZED BY CHARLES DICKENS

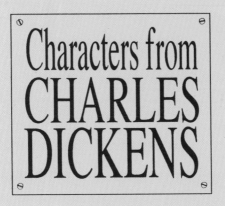

Characters from CHARLES DICKENS

Introduction by
Rob Linn

Illustrations from the
P F Sunman Nostalgia Collection

It does not matter that Dickens'
world is not life-like; it is alive.
Lord Cecil (1902-86)

ISBN 0 947338 53 5

Copyright © Axiom Publishing, Australia.

This edition published 1994 exclusively for Selecta Book Ltd,
Folly Road, Roundway, Devizes, Wiltshire, UK.

FOREWORD

This book contains illustrations of Dickens' characters from the P.F. Sunman Nostalgia Collection.

Not all of Charles Dickens' stories are here represented, but the publisher trusts that the characters presented will provoke fond memories, delight and give pleasure to Dickens readers and enthusiasts.

Serjeant Buzfuz
Pickwick Papers

INTRODUCTION

Charles Dickens portrayed the heart of nineteenth century England and gave life to every aspect of it.

The people, the places, the events, the scenery are, while partly works of his amazing imagination, a living testimony to an era. Here, in Dickens' writings, has been captured for all time the daily life of a nation at the 'grass roots'; for central to all books are the characters of the people, their daily grind, their tussles with life and the struggles of their emotions. They are alive.

Virtually every person that Dickens portrayed has had every detail of their appearance, character, habit, manner of speaking and place of abode, provided by the author.

Take, for example, that 'umble' example of humanity, the treacherous Uriah Heep in *David Copperfield*. Dickens called him 'that crawling impersonation of meanness', with the 'ill-favoured smile upon his face'. There has, perhaps, never been such an apt description of a sneaking, conniving character—the embodiment of selfish ambition—as Uriah Heep. One can sense the very hypocrisy of that fawning, grasping personality.

At the other end of the personality spectrum from Heep were the likes of Captain Cuttle and Florence in that classic portrayal of dashed hopes and high emotion, *Dombey and Son*. Florence, the beautiful girl, whose businessman father had wanted nothing more than an heir to his commercial enterprise, had been left 'an outcast from a living parent's love'. As she grew in stature and beauty and as her father's life crumbled, she met, in the back streets of London, a kindness and affection unknown in that cold tomb of a house which was her father's home.

Captain Cuttle was one of those who befriended her. The description Dickens gave of this hoary old son of the sea preserved the sailor for eternity: 'The captain was one of those timber-looking men, suits of oak as well as hearts, whom it is almost impossible for the liveliest imagination to separate from any part of their dress, however insignificant... the hard glazed hat... and the shirt-collar like a sail, and the wide suit of blue'. It was Cuttle who coined that wonderful statement, 'in the Proverbs of Solomon you will find the following words, "May we never want a friend in need, nor a bottle to give him!" When found, make a note of.'

And what of Scrooge, in *A Christmas Carol*, that tight-fisted man who, until shaken by the ghostly intruders, could not find an ounce of sympathy in his heart for another human being. Of course, there was also, in that same tale, Tiny Tim, whose 'God bless us every one!', described, exactly, the happiness of his household.

Dickens is primarily about the people and places of England which surrounded him; for, again and again, his writing exposed the heart of humanity.

At times, this revelation was not pleasant. That filthy, sodden nurse, Sarah Gamp, for example, was a prime indication of the horrors of society. When she exclaimed, 'He'd make a lovely corpse', the reader can only turn away from her perverse view of life. *Martin Chuzzlewit*, the book in which Sarah Gamp appears, is very much an expose of a side of life in Victorian England which few would want to face. Yet, fundamentally, it is Dickens' use of his characters which so startle us the readers.

While all of Dickens' characters are unforgettable, from his first publications he engaged another means of providing the public with an idea of the images he wished to convey. The illustrations which accompanied his text, drawn by some of the greatest engravers and artists of the time effectively capture the spirit of his words. It is as though the London and England of yesteryear live on in both word and picture.

Two of those illustrators are important in the context of this book of drawings and quotations: Kyd, whose real name was J. Clayton Clark; and Frances Brundage, one of the great women illustrators of post cards. Working in the late nineteenth and early twentieth centuries, they provided the huge audience of English-speaking peoples who idolised Dickens, with an interpretation of the characters in the author's work.

While Kyd was best known for his drawings of Dickens' characters, Frances Brundage also specialised in depictions of children.

Whatever their individual gifts and qualities, their drawings delight to this day and assist to immortalise the world of Charles Dickens, which is forever England.

A Christmas Carol

Alas for Tiny Tim, he bore a little crutch, and had his limbs supported by an iron frame!

* * *

"I have known him to walk with—I have known him to walk with Tiny Tim upon his shoulders, very fast indeed."

* * *

All this time the chestnuts and the jug went round and round; and by and by they had a song, about a lost child travelling in the snow, from Tiny Tim, who had a plaintive little voice, and sang it very well, indeed.

Tim Cratchit (Tiny Tim)

Dombey and Son

Paul

What are the wild waves saying,
Sister, the whole day long,
That ever amid our playing
I hear their low lone song?
Not by the sea-side only,
There it sounds wild and free,
But at night, when it's dark and lonely,
In dreams it is still with me!

Florence

Brother, I hear no singing!
'Tis but the roaring wave,
Ever its long course winging
Over some ocean cave.
'Tis but the noise of water,
Dashing against the shore,
And the wind from some bleaker quarter
Mingling with its roar.

Duet

No! it is something greater
That speaks to the heart alone,
That voice of the great Creator
Dwells in that mighty tone!

This Poem by Joseph Edwards Carpenter written about 1850

FEBRUARY

Sun. –	2	9	16	23
Mon. –	3	10	17	24
Tue. –	4	11	18	25
Wed. –	5	12	19	26
Thu. –	6	13	20	27
Fri. –	7	14	21	28
Sat. 1	8	15	22	29

"I want to know what it says
The sea, Flov. what is it that
it keeps on saying?"

Paul   Dombey and Son

Little Paul & Florence Dombey

Nicholas Nickleby

Mrs Kenwigs was considered a very desirable person to know, and was the constant theme of all the gossips in the street, and even three or four doors round the corner at both ends.

*   *   *

We've got a private master comes to teach us at home, but we ain't proud, because ma says it's sinful.

[Mrs Kenwigs]

MARCH

Sun.	1	8	15	22	29
Mon.	2	9	16	23	30
Tue.	3	10	17	24	31
Wed.	4	11	18	25	–
Thu.	5	12	19	26	–
Fri.	6	13	20	27	–
Sat.	7	14	21	28	–

"I can - not help it,

and it don't signify,

oh! they're too beautiful

to live, much too beautiful!"

Mrs Kenwigs. Nicholas Nickleby.

Mrs Kenwigs

Our Mutual Friend

Her real name was Fanny Cleaver; but she had long ago chosen to bestow upon herself the appellation of Miss Jenny Wren.

* * *

He'd be sharper than a serpent's tooth, if he wasn't as dull as ditch water.

[Jenny Wren]

* * *

"I have been thinking," Jenny went on, "as I sat at work to-day, what a thing it would be if I should be able to have your company till I am married, ar at least courted. Because when I am courted, I shall make Him do some of the things that you do for me..."

APRIL

Sun.	-	5	12	19	26
Mon.	-	6	13	20	27
Tue.	-	7	14	21	28
Wed.	1	8	15	22	29
Thu.	2	9	16	23	30
Fri.	3	10	17	24	-
Sat.	4	11	18	25	-

"Oh, my blessed children, it's poor me
Have pity on me
Take me up and make me light!"

Jenny Wren — Our Mutual Friend

Fanny Cleaver (Jenny Wren)

David Copperfield

Little Em' ly consenting, and allowing me to kiss her, I became desperate; informing her, I recollect, that I should never love another, and that I was prepared to shed the blood of anybody who should aspire to her affections.
[David Copperfield]

*   *   *

At length, when the term of my visit was nearly expired, it was given out that Peggotty and Mr Barkis were going to make a day's holiday together, and that little Em' ly and I were to accompany them. I had but a broken sleep the night before, in anticipation of the pleasure of a whole day with Em' ly.
[David Copperfield]

MAY

Sun.	-	3	10	17	24	31
Mon.	-	4	11	18	25	-
Tue.	-	5	12	19	26	-
Wed.	-	6	13	20	27	-
Thu.	-	7	14	21	28	-
Fri.	1	8	15	22	29	-
Sat.	2	9	16	23	30	-

"I told Emily I adored her
and that unless she confessed she adored me
I should be reduced to the necessity of killing
myself with a sword"

David   David Copperfield

David Copperfield & Little Em'ly

Little Dorrit

Her face was not exceedingly ugly, though it was only redeemed from being so by a smile; a good-humoured smile, and pleasant in itself, but rendered pitiable by being constantly there.

* * *

"What are you doing with the child?" she said to Maggy.

"What are you doing with yourself?" retorted Maggy, for want of a better answer.

"Can't you see, without my telling you?"

"I don't know as I can," said Maggy.

"Killing myself. Now I have answered you, answer me. What are you doing with the child?"

The supposed child kept her head drooped down, and kept her form close at Maggy's side.

"Oh it's all very fine for you,
        little mother,
but I'm a poor thing,
    only ten years old"

Maggie   Little Dorrit

JUNE

Sun.	-	7	14	21	28
Mon.	1	8	15	22	29
Tue.	2	9	16	23	30
Wed.	3	10	17	24	-
Thu.	4	11	18	25	-
Fri.	5	12	19	26	-
Sat.	6	13	20	27	-

Maggy

The Old Curiosity Shop

"Let us be beggars," said the child passing an arm round his neck, "I have no fear but we shall have enough, I am sure we shall. Let us walk through country places, and sleep in fields and under trees, and never think of money again, or anything that can make you sad, but rest at nights, and have the sun and wind upon our faces in the day, and thank God together. Let us never set foot in dark rooms or melancholy houses any more...I will go and beg for both."

JULY

Sun.	-	5	12	19	26
Mon.	-	6	13	20	27
Tue.	-	7	14	21	28
Wed.	1	8	15	22	29
Thu.	2	9	16	23	30
Fri.	3	10	17	24	31
Sat.	4	11	18	25	-

"We are quite safe now, and have nothing
to fear, indeed, dear grandfather."

Little Nell   The Old Curiosity Shop

Nell Trent (Little Nell)

The Cricket On The Hearth

Caleb Plummer and his Blind Daughter lived all alone by themselves, in a little cracked nutshell of a wooden house, which was, in truth, no better than a pimple on the prominent red-brick nose of Gruff and Tackleton...the great feature of the street; but you might have knocked down Caleb Plummer's dwelling with a hammer or two, and carried the pieces off in a cart.

* * *

The blind girl [Bertha] *never knew that iron was rusting, wood rotting, paper peeling off; the size, and shape, and true proportion of the dwelling, withering away...that Caleb's scanty hairs were turning greyer and more grey, before her sightless face.*

Tired what should
tire me, Bertha?

I was never tired

What does it mean?

Caleb Plummer.   The Cricket on the Hearth.

AUGUST

Sun.	–	2	9	16	23 30
Mon.	–	3	10	17	24 31
Tue.	–	4	11	18	25 –
Wed.	–	5	12	19	26 –
Thu.	–	6	13	20	27 –
Fri.	–	7	14	21	28 –
Sat	1	8	15	22	29 –

Caleb & Bertha Plummer

Great Expectations

My father's family name being Pirrip, and
my Christian name Philip, my infant tongue
could make of both names nothing longer or
more explicit than Pip. So, I called myself
Pip, and came to be called Pip.

* * *

"You're not a deceiving imp? You brought
no one with you?"

"No, sir! No!"

"Nor giv' no one office to follow you?"

"No!"

"Well," said he, "I believe you. You'd be but
a fierce young hound indeed, if at your time
of life you could help to hunt a wretched
warmint, hunted as near death and dunghill
as this poor wretched warmint is!"

"He did not turn me upside down, this time,
to get at what I had,
but left me right side
upwards while I opened the bundle and
emphed my pockets."

Pip. Great Expectations

SEPTEMBER

Sun.	–	6	13	20	27
Mon.	–	7	14	21	28
Tue.	1	8	15	22	29
Wed.	2	9	16	23	30
Thu.	3	10	17	24	–
Fri.	4	11	18	25	–
Sat.	5	12	19	26	–

Philip Pirrip (Pip)

The Holly-Tree

And the courage of the boy! Bless your soul, he'd have throwed off his little hat, and tucked up his little sleeves, and gone in at a Lion, he would, if they had happened to meet one, and she [Norah] *had been frightened of him.*

* * *

"Norah dear," said Master Harry, "this is curious. We really ought to see Love Lane. Put on your bonnet, my sweet darling, and we will go there..."

* * *

"Adorable Norah, kiss me, and say you love me to distraction, or I'll jump in head foremost."

OCTOBER

Sun.	–	4	11	18 25
Mon.	–	5	12	19 26
Tue.	–	6	13	20 27
Wed.	–	7	14	21 28
Thu.	1	8	15	22 29
Fri.	2	9	16	23 30
Sat.	3	10	17	24 31

"Norah has always been accustomed to half a glass
of currant wine at dessert. And so have I."

Master Harry   The Holly Tree

Master Harry Walmers

Bleak House

Name, Jo. Nothing else that he knows on. Don't know that everybody has two names. Never heard of sich a think. Don't know that Jo is short for a longer name. Thinks it long enough for him. He don't find no fault with it. Spell it? No. He can't spell it. No father, no mother, no friends. Never been to school. What's home?

* * *

"Now, I know where you live," says the constable, then, to Jo. "You live down in Tom-all-Alone's. That's a nice innocent place to live in, ain't it?"

"I can't go and live in no nicer place, sir," replies Jo. "They wouldn't have nothink to say to me if I wos to go to a nice innocent place fur to live. Who ud go and let a nice innocent lodging to such a reg'lar as me!"

"You are very poor, ain't you?" says the constable.

"Yes, I am indeed, sir, wery poor in gin'ral," replies Jo.

NOVEMBER

Sun.	1	8	15	22	29
Mon.	2	9	16	23	30
Tue.	3	10	17	24	–
Wed.	4	11	18	25	–
Thu.	5	12	19	26	–
Fri.	6	13	20	27	–
Sat.	7	14	21	28	–

They're all
a-watching, and
a-driving of me
Every one of em's
doing of it,
from the time when
I don't get up, to the time when I don't go to bed.
And I'm a-going somewheres. That's where, I'm a-going.

Jo. Bleak House.

Jo (Toughey)

The Chimes

A weak, small, spare old man, he was a very Hercules, this Toby, in his good intentions. He loved to earn his money. He delighted to believe—Toby was very poor, and couldn't well afford to part with a delight—that he was worth his salt. With a shilling or an eighteen-penny message or small parcel in his hand, his courage, always high, rose higher.

* * *

"If I hear 'em, what does it matter whether they speak it or not? Why bless you, my dear," said Toby, pointing at the tower with his fork, and becoming more animated under the influence of dinner, "how often have I heard them bells say, 'Toby Veck, Toby Veck, keep a good heart, Toby! Toby Veck, Toby Veck, keep a good heart, Toby!' A million times? More!"

DECEMBER

Sun.	–	6	13	20	27
Mon.	–	7	14	21	28
Tue.	1	8	15	22	29
Wed.	2	9	16	23	30
Thu.	3	10	17	24	31
Fri.	4	11	18	25	–
Sat.	5	12	19	26	–

"There's nothing more regular in coming round
than dinner-time, and nothing less regular
in coming round than dinner
That's the great difference between 'em"

Toby Veck   The Chimes

Toby Veck (Trotty)

Nicholas Nickleby

He had but one eye, and the popular prejudice runs in favour of two. The eye he had, was unquestionably useful, but decidedly not ornamental; being of a greenish grey, and in shape resembling the fan-light of a street door.

* * *

Subdue your appetites, my dears, and you've conquered human nature.
[Mr Squeers]

* * *

C-l-e-a-n, clean, verb active, to make bright, to scour. W-i-n, win, d-e-r, der, winder, a casement. When the boy knows this out of the book, he goes and does it.
[Mr Squeers]

Wackford Squeers

Oliver Twist

Mr Sikes spoke in the very harshest key of a very harsh voice; but, appeared to entertain some unaccountable objection to having his throat cut...

* * *

"Wolves tear your throats!" muttered Sikes, grinding his teeth. "I wish I was among some of you; you'd howl the hoarser for it."

As Sikes growled forth this imprecation, with the most desperate ferocity that his desperate nature was capable of, he rested the body of the wounded boy across his bended knee; and turned his head, for an instant, to look back at his pursuers.

Bill Sikes

Pickwick Papers

Mrs Bardell—the relict and sole executrix of a deceased custom-house officer—was a comely woman of bustling manners and agreeable appearance, with a natural genius for cooking, improved by study and long practice, into an exquisite talent. There were no children, no servants, no fowls.

*   *   *

Mrs Bardell could only reply by a look. She had long worshipped Mr Pickwick at a distance, but here she was, all at once, raised to a pinnacle to which her wildest and most extravagant hopes had never dared to aspire. Mr Pickwick was going to propose—a deliberate plan, too—sent her little boy to the Borough, to get him out of the way—how thoughtful—how considerate!

Mrs Martha Bardell

Dombey and Son

Train up a fig-tree in the way it should go, and when you are old sit under the shade of it.

[Captain Cuttle]

* * *

"Wal'r, my boy," replied the Captain, "in the Proverbs of Solomon, you will find the following words, 'May we never want a friend in need, nor a bottle to give him!' When found, make a note of."

Here the Captain stretched out his hand to Walter, with an air of downright good faith that spoke volumes; at the same time repeating (for he felt proud of the accuracy and pointed application of his quotation), "When found, make a note of."

Captain Cuttle

The Old Curiosity Shop

His attire was not, as he himself hinted, remarkable for the nicest arrangement, but was in a state of disorder which strongly induced the idea that he had gone to bed in it.

*   *   *

I believe, Sir, that you desire to look at these apartments. They are very charming apartments, Sir. They command an uninterrupted view of—of over the way, and they are within one minute's walk of—of the corner of the street.

[Dick Swiveller]

*   *   *

Fan the sinking flame of hilarity with the wing of friendship; and pass the rosy wine.

[Dick Swiveller]

Dick Swiveller

Oliver Twist

Oliver Twist has asked for more!
[Mr Bumble]

* * *

"Oh, you know, Mr Bumble, he must be mad," said Mrs Sowerberry. "No boy in half his senses could venture to speak so to you."

"It's not Madness, ma'am," replied Mr Bumble, after a few moments of deep meditation. "It's Meat."

"What?" exclaimed Mrs Sowerberry.

"Meat, ma'am, meat," replied Bumble, with stern emphasis. "You've over-fed him, ma'am. You've raised a artificial soul and spirit in him... What have paupers to do with soul or spirit? It's quite enough that we let 'em have live bodies. If you had kept the boy on gruel, ma'am, this would never have happened."

* * *

"If the law supposes that," said Mr Bumble... "the law is a ass — a idiot."

Mr Bumble

The Old Curiosity Shop

"This Marchioness," said Mr Swiveller, folding his arms, "is a very extraordinary person—surrounded by mysteries, ignorant of the taste of beer, unacquainted with her own name (which is less remarkable), and taking a limited view of society through the key-holes of doors—can these things be her destiny, or has some unknown person started an opposition to the decrees of fate? It is a most inscrutable and unmitigated staggerer!"

The Marchioness

Pickwick Papers

Mr Pickwick observed that fame was dear to the heart of every man... The praise of mankind was his [Pickwick's] Swing; philanthropy was his insurance office.

*   *   *

"I am ruminating," said Mr Pickwick, "on the strange mutability of human affairs.'

"Ah! I see—in at the palace door one day, out at the window the next. Philosopher, sir?"

"An observer of human nature, sir," said Mr Pickwick.

Samuel Pickwick

David Copperfield

The only subject...on which he ever showed a violent temper or swore an oath, was this generosity of his; and if it were ever referred to...he would be 'Gormed' if he didn't cut and run for good, if it was ever mentioned again.

* * *

I'm Gormed—and I can't say no fairer than that!

[Mr Peggotty]

* * *

"You have quite made up your mind," said I to Mr Peggotty, "as to the future, good friend? I need scarcely ask you."

"Quite, Mas'r Davy," he returned; "and told Em'ly. Theer's mighty countries fur from here. Our future life lays over the sea... No one can't reproach my darling in Australia. We will begin a new life over theer!"

Daniel Peggotty

Oliver Twist

He wore a man's coat, which reached nearly
to his heels. He had turned the cuffs back,
half-way up his arm, to get his hands out of
the sleeves: apparently with the ultimate view
of thrusting them into the pockets of his
corduroy trousers; for there he kept them.

* * *

"Come on,' said the jailer.

"Oh ah! I'll come on," replied the Dodger,
brushing his hat with the palm of his hand.
"Ah! (to the Bench) it's no use your looking
frightened; I won't show you no mercy, not a
ha'porth of it. You'll pay for this, my fine
fellers. I wouldn't be you for something! I
wouldn't go free, now, if you was to fall down
on your knees and ask me. Here, carry me off
to prison! Take me away!'

John Dawkins (The Artful Dodger)

Martin Chuzzlewit

Let us be moral. Let us contemplate existence.

[Seth Pecksniff]

*   *   *

"The name of those fabulous animals (pagan, I regret to say) who used to sing in the water, has quite escaped me." Mr George Chuzzlewit suggested "Swans." "No," said Mr Pecksniff. "Not swans. Very like swans, too. Thank you." The nephew...propounded "Oysters." "No," said Mr Pecksniff,... "nor oysters. But by no means unlike oysters; a vey excellent idea; thank you, my dear sir, very much. Wait. Sirens! Dear me! sirens, of course."

Seth Pecksniff

Martin Chuzzlewit

Some people...may be Rooshans, and others may be Prooshans; they are born so, and will please themselves. Them which is of other naturs thinks different.

[Mrs Sarah Gamp]

*　*　*

...leave the bottle on the chimley-piece, and don't ask me to take none, but let me put my lips to it when I am so dispoged.

[Mrs Sarah Gamp]

*　*　*

"She's the sort of woman now," said Mould, "one would almost feel disposed to bury for nothing: and do it neatly, too!"

Mrs Sarah Gamp

Dombey and Son

Unless young Toots had some idea on the subject, to the expression of which he was wholly unequal. Ideas, like ghosts (according to the common notion of ghosts), must be spoken to a little before they will explain themselves; and Toots had long left off asking any questions of his own mind...

"How are you?" he would say to Paul, fifty times a day.

"Quite well, Sir, thank you," Paul would answer.

"Shake hands," would be Toots's next advance.

Which Paul, of course, would immediately do. Mr Toots generally said again, after a long interval of staring and hard breathing, "How are you?" To which Paul again replied, "Quite well, Sir, thank you."

Toots

David Copperfield

I am well aware that I am the 'umblest person going. ...My mother is likewise a very 'umble person. We live in a numble abode.

[Uriah Heep]

* * *

As I came back I saw Uriah Heep shutting up the office, and feeling friendly towards everybody, went in and spoke to him, and at parting gave him my hand. But oh, what a clammy hand his was! as ghostly to the touch as to the sight! I rubbed mine afterwards to warm it, and to rub his off.

[David Copperfield]

Uriah Heep

The Old Curiosity Shop

Mr Quilp could scarcely be said to be of any particular trade or calling, though his pursuits were diversified and his occupations numerous. He collected the rents of whole colonies of filthy streets and alleys by the waterside...

*　　*　　*

"It's very true," said Quilp, "that your grandfather urged repeated forgiveness, ingratitude, riot, and extravagance, and all that; but as I told him 'these are common faults.'..."

Daniel Quilp

Pickwick Papers

"What's your name, sir?" inquired the judge.

"Sam Weller, my lord," replied that gentle-man.

"Do you spell it with a 'V' or a 'W'?" inquired the judge.

"That depends upon the taste and fancy of the speller, my lord," replied Sam...

*   *   *

"Yes, I have a pair of eyes," replied Sam, "and that's just it. If they wos a pair o' patent double million magnifyin' gas microscopes of hextra power, p'raps I might be able to see through a flight o' stairs and a deal door; but bein' only eyes, you see my wision's limited."

Samuel Weller

"It is a far, far better thing that I do, than I have ever done; it is a far, far better rest that I go to, than I have ever known."

Sydney Carton
A Tale Of Two Cities